D0964103

© 2002 Algrove Publishing Limited
ALL RIGHTS RESERVED.
No part of this book may be reproduced in any form, including photocopying, without permission in writing from the publishers, except by a reviewer who may quote brief passages in a magazine or newspaper or on radio or television.

Algrove Publishing Limited
1090 Morrison Drive
Ottawa, Ontario
Canada K2H 1C2

National Library of Canada Cataloguing in Publication Data

Williams, J. R. (James Robert), 1888-1957
  The Bull of the Woods / J.R. Williams.

(Classic reprint series)
Reprint of ed. originally published: New York : C. Scribner's Sons, 1933.
ISBN 1-894572-61-0

   1. American wit and humor, Pictorial. 2. Machinists–Caricatures and cartoons. I. Title. II. Series: Classic reprint series (Ottawa, Ont.)

NC1429.W573A4 2002   741.5'973   C2002-903623-2

Printed in Canada
#21002

Publisher's Note

James Robert Williams was born in Nova Scotia in 1887. He ran away from home in his mid-teens, worked on a ranch for a while, then spent three years with the U.S. Cavalry. After he married, he took a full-time job with a crane manufacturing company in Ohio. He became a full-time cartoonist in 1921, continuing to draw *Out Our Way* and other series until his death in 1957.

Leonard G. Lee, Publisher
Ottawa
August, 2002

THE
BULL OF THE WOODS

J. R. WILLIAMS

NEW YORK
CHARLES SCRIBNER'S SONS
1944

FOREWORD

The term "Bull of the Woods" was borrowed from the lumber-jacks. I used it to describe a gruff, poker-faced man prowling among hundreds of machine belts in a shop in Alliance, Ohio. Silhouetted against the hazy shop windows, they had a certain resemblance to a dense woods.

The "Bull" was hardboiled, perhaps, but he was kind. He must have been, or I certainly should have been fired. He said to me one day with fine sarcasm, "Pardon my rudeness. You've been turning out two cartoons and one shaft a day on this machine. Couldn't you make it two shafts and one cartoon a day? This is a machine shop."

And now, when I have no shafts to do, I have a terrible time turning out one cartoon a day.

J. R. WILLIAMS

THE INSIDE DOPE

J.R.WILLIAMS

10-10

THE SELF-WORKER.

THE INVALIDS

THE PLEASURE LOVER.

HEROES ARE MADE—NOT BORN

THE KING'S HORSES.

THE ONE-HORSE WAGON

J.R WILLIAMS

4-25

THE SAVERS.

HALF TIME.

THE STANDSTILL

THE BLINDERS

J.P. WILLIAMS
6-28

THE BOUQUET

J.R. WILLIAMS

11-30

THE FISH MARKET

J.R.WILLIAMS   2-9

THE MAN WITH THE WHOA

THE FINANCIER

J.R.WILLIAMS
2-3

THE HUMAN TOUCH

THE FINISHING TOUCH.

INDUSTRY.

J.R.WILLIAMS 9

FOR ANGELS ONLY.

1-18

J.R.WILLIAMS

THE ROAD TO GLORY

THE BORROWER

THE TWO-TIMER

THE UPPER CRUST.   4-14   J.R.WILLIAMS

THE BOOSTER.

8-3
J.R.WILLIAMS

HEROES ARE MADE—NOT BORN

PARTNERS IN CRIME

J.R.WILLIAMS

12-28

THE LOVER

J.R. WILLIAMS
12-21

THE GOOD GUY?

THE SPEED KING.

J.R.WILLIAMS

THE GRINDLESS GRIND

THE RAINBOW'S END

ADVICE

J.R.WILLIAMS
1-12

INDOOR TAN

9-1

THE CRAMP

J.P.WILLIAMS
3-17

THE SOCIAL BARRIERS

THE PICKER

WRONG EITHER WAY

THE EELIGHT.

STRANGE BED-FELLOWS

J.R.WILLIAMS
7-4

THE LONG ROAD AND THE SHORT

THE TEACHERS

THE "SOONER"

J.R.WILLIAMS
4-28

THE MOVING COLUMNS

J.R.WILLIAMS
2-14

THE BUGLER

THE FATHEAD DEPARTMENT

CURIOSITY

THE EXTRA SHIFT

SHERIDAN'S RIDE

J.R.WILLIAMS
9-25

AND A SOLDIER GETS THE GUARDHOUSE

OLD IRON

J. R. WILLIAMS

5-28

HIGH FINANCE

J.R.WILLIAMS
2-26

THE FEMININE TOUCH

HEROES ARE MADE--NOT BORN

THE WORRIER

THE WEED KILLERS

J.R.WILLIAMS
12-19

THE ACCESSORY

THE STRANGER

J.R.WILLIAMS
11-28

BORN THIRTY YEARS TOO SOON

THE BEAUTY PACKS

THE FAST WORKER

THE MAN OF THE HOUR

J. R. WILLIAMS

1-8

THE SHELF ROBBERS

J.R.WILLIAMS

5-22

HEROES ARE MADE, NOT BORN

HEROES ARE MADE NOT BORN

SPOILIN' 'EM

BORN THIRTY YEARS TOO SOON

MEMORY LANE

J.R.WILLIAMS

3-5

THE BED SPREAD

J.R.WILLIAMS

4-23

THE SECOND START

ALONE IN A CROWD

"ENGINEERING"

OVERACTING

J.R. WILLIAMS
8-13

A NATIONAL TRAIT

J.R.WILLIAMS
3-26

BORN THIRTY YEARS TOO SOON   J.R.WILLIAMS

1-3

THE BROKEN CHAIN

BORN THIRTY YEARS TOO SOON   12-21 J.R.WILLIAMS

THE MAGICIAN

J.R.WILLIAMS

12-17

WAR EFFICIENCY

J.R.WILLIAMS   4-18

MYSTERIES OF LIFE

THE ART EXHIBIT

J.P.WILLIAMS

12-25

BORN THIRTY YEARS TOO SOON   7-16   J.R.WILLIAMS

WINNERS MAKE LOSERS.

THE ECONOMIST

J.R.WILLIAMS

3-15

THE BOMBER

THE OLD CHIEF

THE OLD RESENTER

TOO MANY COOKS

"MACHINISTS WANTED"

THE BIG GUY

THE BALKER

10-15   J.R.WILLIAMS

READING MATTER

J.R.WILLIAMS

7-24

THE UTOPIAN

FORCE OF HABIT.

BORN THIRTY YEARS TOO SOON   J.R. WILLIAMS

THE SAFE DISTANCE

J.R. WILLIAMS
11-21

WORKING STUDENTS.

THE GENIUS.

J.R.WILLIAMS

COLD STEEL

THE DIPLOMAT

J.R.WILLIAMS
4-26

"COITINS"

THE CAT AND MICE

THE ARMY OF GENERALS

5-11

J.R.WILLIAMS

THE LONE STAR

PAPER PROPHETS

J.R.WILLIAMS

2-15

THE BURIED PAST

J.R. WILLIAMS
7-17

MOUTHS AND HEARTS

J.R.WILLIAMS
11-9

HEROES ARE MADE—NOT BORN.

THE NEW OUTLOOK AND THE OLD LOOKOUT

THE BULL O' TH' WOODS

HOMINESS

THE WORD PICTURE

6-21

J.R.WILLIAMS

THE KING'S HENCHMEN